THE ULTIMATE
TAMPA BAY BUCCANEERS
TRIVIA BOOK

A Collection of Amazing Trivia Quizzes
and Fun Facts for Die-Hard Bucs Fans!

Ray Walker

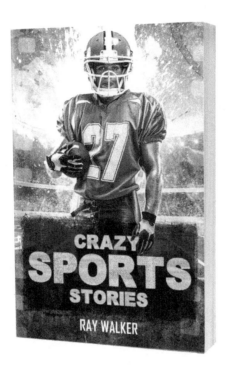

CONTENTS

INTRODUCTION

Team fandom should be inspirational. Our attachment to our favorite teams should fill us with pride, excitement, loyalty, and a sense of fulfillment in knowing that we are part of a community with many other fans who feel the same way.

Tampa Bay Buccaneers fans are no exception. With a rich, successful history in the NFL, the Buccaneers have inspired their supporters to strive for greatness with their tradition of colorful players, memorable eras, big moves, and unique moments.

This book is meant to be a celebration of those moments, and an examination of the collection of interesting, impressive, or important details that allow us to understand the full stories behind the players and the team.

You may use the book as you wish. Each chapter contains 20 quiz questions in a mixture of multiple-choice and true-false formats, an answer key (Don't worry, it's on a separate page!), and a section of 10 "Did You Know?" factoids about the team.

Some will use it to test themselves with the quiz questions. How much Buccaneers history did you really know? How many of the finer points can you remember? Some will use it competitively (Isn't that the heart of sports?), waging contests with friends and fellow devotees to see who can lay claim to being the biggest fan. Some will enjoy it as a learning experience, gaining insight to enrich their fandom and add color to their understanding of their favorite team. Still others may use it to teach, sharing the wonderful anecdotes inside to inspire a new generation of fans to hop aboard the Buccaneers bandwagon.

Whatever your purpose may be, we hope you enjoy delving into the amazing background of Tampa Bay Buccaneers football!

Oh… For the record, information and statistics in this book are current up to the beginning of 2021. The Bucs will surely topple more records and win more awards as the seasons pass, so keep this in mind when you're watching the next game with your friends, and someone starts a conversation with "Did you know…?" to share some trivia.

CHAPTER 1:

ORIGINS & HISTORY

QUIZ TIME!

1. In which year did the Buccaneers begin playing in the National Football League?

   a. 1960
   b. 1970
   c. 1976
   d. 1983

2. The franchise was nearly called the Tampa Bay Gators, partially because of the widespread number of alligators native to the region, and partially to tap into the local support and goodwill toward the University of Florida program with that name.

   a. True
   b. False

3. How was the nickname "Buccaneers" chosen as the team's official moniker?

a. Through a radio contest, with the entry based on the pirates who had been central to Florida's history

b. By the team founder, who considered himself an adventurer in the world of business

c. As a corporate tie-in, because the team's owner had made part of his fortune with a shipbuilding company called Buccaneer Holdings

d. As a marketing tactic, playing off the success of the hugely popular 1972 Orson Welles movie *Treasure Island*

4. In which season did the Buccaneers begin to play at their new field (Raymond James Stadium) after moving from their longtime home at Tampa Stadium?

   a. 1996
   b. 1998
   c. 2002
   d. 2003

5. Who was the founder of the Tampa Bay Buccaneers?

   a. Robert Irsay
   b. John McKay
   c. Malcolm Glazer
   d. Hugh Culverhouse

6. In which season did the Buccaneers earn their first-ever NFL playoff berth?

   a. 1976
   b. 1979

c. 1997

d. 2002

7. The Tampa Bay Buccaneers won more regular-season football games than any other NFL team during the period between 1995 and 2005.

   a. True

   b. False

8. How many times in their franchise history have the Tampa Bay Buccaneers won a division title?

   a. 1

   b. 3

   c. 6

   d. 11

9. Who was the first Buc ever to be named a First Team All-Pro by the Associated Press?

   a. Defensive end Lee Roy Selmon

   b. Quarterback Vinny Testaverde

   c. Linebacker Derrick Brooks

   d. Linebacker Dave Lewis

10. Where do the Tampa Bay Buccaneers rank among NFL franchises when it comes to most Super Bowl appearances?

    a. 4th overall

    b. Tied for 9th overall

    c. Tied for 18th overall

    d. 29th overall

11. How did the Buccaneers fare during their 30th anniversary season in the NFL?

    a. Missed the playoffs

    b. Lost in the Wild Card game against Washington

    c. Lost in the divisional playoffs against Green Bay

    d. Won the Super Bowl against Kansas City

12. The longest stretch the Buccaneers have gone without making the playoffs is 14 years, which occurred between 1983 and 1996.

    a. True

    b. False

13. Which team, that has since moved, did Tampa Bay face in its first-ever NFL game (which resulted in a 20-0 shutout loss for the Bucs)?

    a. San Diego Chargers

    b. Baltimore Colts

    c. Houston Oilers

    d. Oakland Raiders

14. What were the details surrounding the Buccaneers' first-ever shutout victory in the NFL?

    a. 1977, the team's second season, in a 14-0 victory over the Chicago Bears

    b. 1979, the team's fourth season, in a 3-0 victory over the Kansas City Chiefs

    c. 1982, the team's seventh season, in a 28-0 victory over the Atlanta Falcons

d. 1983, the team's eighth season, in a 17-0 victory over the Cleveland Browns

15. Which player kicked the first-ever successfully made field goal for the Tampa Bay Buccaneers?

    a. Van Tiffin
    b. Obed Ariri
    c. Dave Green
    d. Garo Yepremian

16. As of 2021, Tampa Bay is tied with Green Bay Packers and Pittsburgh Steelers as the franchises that have sent more players to the Pro Bowl than any other NFL franchise.

    a. True
    b. False

17. How did Tampa Bay fare in its first-ever NFL playoff run?

    a. Lost in the first round against the Dallas Cowboys
    b. Lost in the divisional playoffs against the Green Bay Packers
    c. Lost in the NFC Championship against the Los Angeles Rams
    d. Won the Super Bowl against the Oakland Raiders

18. What is Tampa Bay's franchise record for most victories recorded by the club in a single regular season?

    a. 10
    b. 11
    c. 12
    d. 13

19. What is the name of the Buccaneers' mascot?

    a. Bucky Blackjack

    b. Peg Leg

    c. Redbeard

    d. Captain Fear

20. The Tampa Bay football franchise has, at some point, been included in both the American Football Conference and the National Football Conference within the NFL's division of teams.

    a. True

    b. False

QUIZ ANSWERS

1. C – 1976

2. B – False

3. A – Through a radio contest, with the entry based on the pirates who had been central to Florida's history

4. B – 1998

5. D – Hugh Culverhouse

6. B – 1979

7. B – False

8. C – 6

9. A – Defensive end Lee Roy Selmon

10. C – Tied for 18th overall

11. B – Lost in the Wild Card game against Washington

12. A – True

13. C – Houston Oilers

14. B – 1979, the team's fourth season, in a 3-0 victory over the Kansas City Chiefs

15. C – Dave Green

16. B – False

17. C – Lost in the NFC Championship against the Los Angeles Rams

18. C – 12

19. D – Captain Fear

20. A – True

DID YOU KNOW?

1. Before Hugh Culverhouse became the first owner of the Tampa Bay Buccaneers, Tampa Bay's expansion team was originally granted to a Philadelphia-based businessman named Tom McCloskey, who backed out of the deal because of financial concerns.

2. Tampa Bay had been the site of several professional football games before the Buccaneers arrived. In 1964, the area held an AFL exhibition game featuring the New York Jets and the Buffalo Bills, and in 1969, the AFL's Miami Dolphins took on the NFL's Minnesota Vikings in a preseason game there. This practice continued into the 1970s as well.

3. Raymond James Stadium, the current home of the Buccaneers, houses a very distinctive 103-foot-long pirate ship that sits in one of its end zones. The ship features cannons that fire, flag poles that display messages, and a parrot that talks to fans.

4. While the Buccaneers are an anchor tenant of Raymond James Stadium, it is not their home exclusively. The NCAA's University of South Florida Bulls also play there, along with the XFL's Tampa Bay Vipers, while the stadium also hosts soccer, equestrian events, concerts, monster truck shows, and even professional wrestling events, like WrestleMania 37 in 2021.

5. As a new team entering the NFL in 1976, the Buccaneers paid a $16 million franchise fee for the right to join the league. For context, when the Houston Texans joined in 2002, they paid an expansion fee of $700 million.

6. Tampa Bay's first-ever touchdown was not scored until the team's fourth NFL game, as they were shut out in their first two contests and only kicked field goals in their third. But on October 3, 1976, defensive back Danny Reece got the Bucs into the end zone for the first time after a 44-yard fumble return touchdown against the Baltimore Colts.

7. According to Buccaneers wide receiver Mike Evans, the New Orleans Saints are Tampa Bay's biggest NFL rival. Evans says "there is a lot of emotion, a lot of physicality. As players, we love it—we love this rivalry." The Saints have the advantage in the head-to-head rivalry, 37-22, but the Buccaneers are undefeated against New Orleans in the playoffs and have also won more championships, so the bragging rights are debatable.

8. Tampa Bay's franchise record for most victories recorded by the club in a single regular season is 12, which they set during the 2002 season.

9. The Buccaneers have a theme song which plays frequently when the team scores at home. The original tune, "Hey, Hey Tampa Bay," was written in 1977 by Jeff Arthur, who also created a new updated version in 1997.

10. In the beginning, the Buccaneers struggled mightily. They finished their first season winless at 0-14, and then posted a 2-12 record the following year. Steady progress led to their first season above .500 in 1979, when the team reached a 10-6 record.

CHAPTER 2:

JERSEYS & NUMBERS

QUIZ TIME!

1. When they began playing in the NFL in 1976, the Buccaneers used what color scheme for both their home and away uniforms?

    a. Orange, white, and red
    b. Orange, green, and black
    c. Gold, silver, and brown
    d. Red, white, and blue

2. The numbers 0 and 00 have been banned from circulation by Tampa Bay's ownership, as they are seen to represent a losing attitude.

    a. True
    b. False

3. How many stripes run from the crown to the back of the neck on the current version of the Buccaneers' helmets?

    a. One red stripe and two white stripes
    b. One orange stripe

c. Three red stripes

d. No stripes are used on these helmets.

4. Which Tampa Bay Buccaneers offensive lineman chose his number with the team because his older brother had worn that number in high school?

   a. Center Ryan Jensen, number 66

   b. Offensive tackle Demar Dotson, number 69

   c. Guard Ali Marpet, number 74

   d. Offensive tackle Donovan Smith, number 76

5. Which of the following player numbers is NOT among those that are out of circulation in Tampa Bay, despite not being officially retired?

   a. Cornerback Ronde Barber's number 20

   b. Fullback Mike Alstott's number 40

   c. Running back Warrick Dunn's number 28

   d. Safety John Lynch's number 47

6. Which jersey number has proven to be most popular with Bucs fans in 2020, having sold the most Tampa Bay jerseys on NFL.com as well as more than any other NFL player except Kansas City Chiefs quarterback Patrick Mahomes?

   a. Wide receiver Mike Evans's number 13

   b. Tight end Rob Gronkowski's number 87

   c. Linebacker Lavonte David's number 54

   d. Quarterback Tom Brady's number 12

7. The pewter jerseys worn by Tampa Bay are often said to have been "jinxed," and therefore, the team avoids wearing them during the Super Bowl whenever the choice is theirs.

a. True

b. False

8. Which new arrival to the Buccaneers made a donation to wide receiver Adam Humphries's favorite charity in order to get Humphries to give up the number 11?

a. Antonio Brown

b. Scotty Miller

c. DeSean Jackson

d. Vincent Jackson

9. The current version of the Buccaneers uniform includes four colors. Which of the following is NOT included in their color scheme?

a. Orange

b. Buccaneer red

c. Platinum

d. Pewter

10. When quarterback Tom Brady, considered by many to be the greatest football player of all time, joined Tampa Bay in 2020, which Buccaneer voluntarily gave up the number 12 that Brady famously wore?

a. Quarterback Blaine Gabbert

b. Kicker Ryan Succop

c. Cornerback Carlton Davis

d. Wide receiver Chris Godwin

11. Twenty players have worn number 81 for the Buccaneers. Which of these players scored the most career touchdowns with the team?

a. Wide receiver Antonio Brown

b. Wide receiver Tim Brown

c. Wide receiver Jacquez Green

d. Tight end Alex Smith

12. Star defensive tackle Warren Sapp is the only Buccaneer to have ever worn the number 99 on his jersey and will continue to be the only one as his number is now retired.

   a. True

   b. False

13. When franchise mainstay Gerald McCoy was let go, his number 93 was not taken out of circulation as many expected, but rather given to which new arrival to the Buccaneers?

   a. Defensive end Jason Pierre-Paul

   b. Linebacker Devin White

   c. Defensive tackle Ndamukong Suh

   d. Safety Antoine Winfield Jr.

14. How many jersey numbers have the Tampa Bay Buccaneers retired for their former players?

   a. 1

   b. 3

   c. 6

   d. 7

15. Which player competed for the Buccaneers for just 121 regular-season games; the shortest tenure of anyone whose number has been retired by the franchise?

a. Defensive end Lee Roy Selmon

b. Defensive tackle Warren Sapp

c. Cornerback Ronde Barber

d. Linebacker Derrick Brooks

16. Eight players have worn the number 1 for Tampa Bay, and every single one of those players was a quarterback.

a. True

b. False

17. Lucky number 7 has been worn by a dozen Buccaneers players over the years. Which athlete wore it for the longest amount of time?

a. Quarterback Jeff Garcia

b. Kicker Patrick Murray

c. Kicker Martin Gramatica

d. Quarterback Craig Erickson

18. Who is the most recent Buccaneers player to have his number retired by the club?

a. Linebacker Derrick Brooks

b. Defensive tackle Warren Sapp

c. Quarterback Doug Williams

d. Defensive end Lee Roy Selmon

19. Which number did star linebacker Derrick Brooks, who was elected to the Pro Football Hall of Fame, wear on the back of his jersey for Tampa Bay?

a. 50

b. 53

c. 55

d. 57

20. The Buccaneers have retired more jersey numbers than any other NFL franchise has.

    a. True

    b. False

QUIZ ANSWERS

1. A – Orange, white, and red

2. B – False

3. D – No stripes are used on these helmets.

4. A – Center Ryan Jensen, number 66

5. C – Running back Warrick Dunn's number 28

6. D – Quarterback Tom Brady's number 12

7. B – False

8. C – DeSean Jackson

9. C – Platinum

10. D – Wide receiver Chris Godwin

11. D – Tight end Alex Smith

12. B – False

13. C – Defensive tackle Ndamukong Suh

14. B – 3

15. A – Defensive end Lee Roy Selmon

16. B – False

17. C – Kicker Martin Gramatica

18. A – Linebacker Derrick Brooks

19. C – 55

20. B – False

DID YOU KNOW?

1. The original Bucs logo featured the face of a pirate (Bucco Bruce), wearing a large hat with a feather in it and holding a dagger between his teeth. This logo stood for 21 years before the team switched to a flag bearing a skull above crossed swords, with a football between them.

2. For many years, the Buccaneers wore an orange and white uniform that was commonly referred to as "The Creamsicle." This was named after a popular frozen treat that featured the same color orange on the outside with a vanilla center.

3. Bucs running back Peyton Barber chose to wear number 25 on his jersey in honor of his favorite player while growing up: USC superstar and New Orleans Saints draft pick Reggie Bush.

4. Tampa Bay's original color scheme, with a bright fluorescent orange and red combination, was chosen to represent the sunshine and citrus industry in their home state of Florida through the orange, and "courage and fortitude in battle" through the red.

5. After Tampa Bay owner Malcolm Glazer's death in 2014, the Buccaneers added a commemorative patch to their jerseys to honor Glazer. The patch was a tasteful black circle with the white initials "MG" in the middle.

6. Buccaneers safety John Lynch is a member of the Pro Football Hall of Fame. He was never elected to the Baseball Hall of Fame, but his jersey does hang there. Lynch was drafted as a pitcher by the expansion Florida Marlins in 1992 and threw the first pitch in that franchise's history with the New York-Penn League's Erie Sailors, which is why his jersey was immortalized despite Lynch never making a big-league appearance.

7. Superstition may have scared some Buccaneers away from wearing the number 13. It has been worn by very few players over the years, most of whom made little impact, but recently, star wide receiver Mike Evans has avoided any curse during his seven seasons sporting the digits.

8. Since 1973, the NFL no longer allows players to wear jersey number 0 or 00. No Tampa Bay Buccaneers ever wore either number as a grandfathered exception to this rule, so neither number will ever be used in franchise history.

9. The highest number ever retired by the Tampa Bay Buccaneers is number 99, belonging to Hall of Fame defensive tackle Warren Sapp.

10. Buccaneers linebacker Derrick Brooks has two different jersey numbers retired. Tampa Bay has put his number 55 out of circulation for good, but in college, Brooks wore number 10, which has also been permanently retired by his alma mater, the Florida State Seminoles.

CHAPTER 3:

CATCHY NICKNAMES

QUIZ TIME!

1. By which nickname are the Buccaneers' fans most commonly referred to?

   a. "The Bucs Backers"

   b. "The Pewter Pirates"

   c. "The Bay Boys"

   d. "The Orange Lunatics"

2. Talented Buccaneers wide receiver Keyshawn Johnson was often referred to as "The Diva" thanks to his me-first attitude and focus on his individual statistics.

   a. True

   b. False

3. The longtime home of the Buccaneers, Raymond James Stadium, is also more commonly known by which popular nickname?

   a. "The Pirate Palace"

   b. "The Dock"

c. "The New Sombrero"

d. "The Buc Barn"

4. Which Tampa Bay Buccaneer is affectionately known by players and fans as "The Gentle Giant"?

   a. Wide receiver Vincent Jackson

   b. Head coach Tony Dungy

   c. Defensive end Lee Roy Selmon

   d. Offensive tackle Paul Kruger

5. Why was Buccaneers cornerback Darrelle Revis known around the league as "Revis Island"?

   a. Because the talented Revis kept to himself and refused to socialize with other teammates

   b. Because he actually bought a small island in the Caribbean and named it after himself

   c. Because it was almost a guarantee that he would be going to Honolulu ("the island") every year to play in the Pro Bowl

   d. Because receivers facing off against him would be marooned there, with few passes coming their way

6. Why was Tampa Bay linebacker Broderick Thomas known to players as "The Sandman"?

   a. Because he owned a large mansion on the beach where he would host parties after many games

   b. Because he was always willing to do the gritty little things that helped his team win games

c. Because he hit hard enough to knock players out and knock the football loose

d. Because he had difficulty staying awake during team meetings and would frequently nod off while coaches were speaking

7. Tampa Bay running back Doug Martin was known as "The Muscle Hamster" because of his chiseled physique and non-stop foot movement, like a hamster on a spinning wheel who would just keep going.

   a. True
   b. False

8. Why was Buccaneers running back Earnest Graham given the nickname "Mr. August" by coach Jon Gruden?

   a. Because he was frequently injured soon after the season started in September

   b. Because he appeared shirtless in a photo for that month in a calendar that the Bucs made for charity

   c. Because he led Tampa Bay in rushing for three consecutive preseasons

   d. Because he was always complaining that it was too hot, no matter when a game or practice was being held

9. Despite having a fun nickname ("The New Sombrero"), Raymond James Stadium is most commonly referred to by which simple nickname by most local citizens and fans of the Buccaneers?

a. "The Field"

b. "Ray Jay"

c. "Tampa 2"

d. "The Jim"

10. Buccaneers defensive tackle Anthony McFarland went by which disgusting one-word nickname?

   a. "Mucous"

   b. "Spitball"

   c. "Snot"

   d. "Booger"

11. Which Buccaneers player was known to fans and teammates by the nickname "The A-Train"?

   a. Defensive end Chidi Ahanotu

   b. Middle linebacker Adam Hayward

   c. Cornerback Donnie Abraham

   d. Running back Mike Alstott

12. After engaging in two memorable fights with his former Cleveland Browns teammates as a newly traded member of the Buccaneers, ex-Browns tight end Kellen Winslow earned the nickname "The Vengeful Ex."

   a. True

   b. False

13. Which Buccaneers kicker was known to teammates by the nickname below because he converted an almost perfect 181 of 183 extra point attempts with Tampa Bay?

   a. Martin "Automatica" Gramatica

   b. Michael "Snack Break" Husted

c. Connor "It's Good" Barth

d. Matt "Mr. Perfect" Bryant

14. Most NFL fans actually knew Buccaneers running back "Cadillac" Williams better by his nickname than his real name, which was actually what?

   a. Deshaun

   b. Eric

   c. Roberto

   d. Carnell

15. An NFL rule informally known as "The Bert Emanuel Rule," named after a controversial play involving the longtime Buccaneers wide receiver, states that which of the following is true?

   a. An offensive player who is an eligible receiver may push off against a defensive player while running his route, but only within five yards of the line of scrimmage.

   b. Players may not remove their helmets on the field of play, even after the whistle is blown, unless they have clearly returned to their own sidelines.

   c. If a receiver keeps control of the football during a catch, the ball is allowed to touch the ground as the catch is made.

   d. While players may wear gloves during the game, neither these gloves nor a player's bare hands may be coated with any substance that provides extra grip for holding onto the football.

16. Tampa Bay quarterback Tom Brady was called "The Godfather" by his young teammates because he was brought in to provide leadership and playoff experience while demonstrating how to act as a professional athlete.

    a. True
    b. False

17. In 2020, the Buccaneers boasted a fearsome defensive backfield. What was this unit's nickname for the year?

    a. "The Great Wall of Tampa"
    b. "Seek and Destroy"
    c. "The Gravediggers"
    d. "Bruce's Bad Boys"

18. One of head coach Jon Gruden's former players gave the coach a nickname that stuck, based on his resemblance to which of the following horror movie characters?

    a. "Freddy Krueger" in the movie *A Nightmare on Elm Street*
    b. "Jason" in the movie *Friday the 13th*
    c. "Leatherface" in the movie *The Texas Chainsaw Massacre*
    d. "Chucky" in the movie *Child's Play*

19. Buccaneers tight end "O.J." Howard is most commonly known by that nickname, because people have trouble pronouncing his real name, which is what?

    a. O'Terrius Jabari
    b. Oneonta Jaskaran

c. Ominus Julius

d. Orville Jorville

20. During some of Tampa Bay's worst seasons, the team was sarcastically referred to not as the "Bucs" but often as the "Succs" or the "Yuccs."

a. True

b. False

QUIZ ANSWERS

1. B – "The Pewter Pirates"

2. B – False

3. C – "The New Sombrero"

4. C – Defensive end Lee Roy Selmon

5. D – Because receivers facing off against him would be marooned there, with few passes coming their way

6. C – Because he hit hard enough to knock players out and knock the football loose

7. A – True

8. C – Because he led Tampa Bay in rushing for three consecutive preseasons

9. B – "Ray Jay"

10. D – "Booger"

11. D – Running back Mike Alstott

12. B – False

13. A – Martin "Automatica" Gramatica

14. D – Carnell

15. C – If a receiver keeps control of the football during a catch, the ball is allowed to touch the ground as the catch is made.

16. B – False

17. C – "The Gravediggers"

18. D – "Chucky" in the movie *Child's Play*

19. A – O'Terrius Jabari

20. A – True

DID YOU KNOW?

1. Buccaneers quarterback Ryan Fitzpatrick was noted for his streaky play and depending on whether the streak was good or bad, he was known as "Fitzmagic" or "Fitztragic."

2. Tampa Bay punter Tom Tupa was known as "Two-Point Tupa" because he was the first kick holder to pick up the ball on extra point attempts and run it into the end zone after the NFL legalized two-point conversions after touchdowns.

3. East Tennessee State University also uses the nickname "Buccaneers," which means that when Tampa Bay selected defensive back Donnie Abraham from the school in 1996, his team nickname did not change upon joining the NFL.

4. During the 1982 NFL season, which was interrupted by the players' strike, the Buccaneers narrowly won five of their last six games to squeak into a playoff format that was expanded due to the unusual year. This team became known as the "Cardiac Kids."

5. When the Buccaneers featured the dynamic Warrick Dunn and the bruising Mike Alstott at running back, they were known by the common nickname "Thunder and Lightning." More creative fans also referred to the duo as "WD-40," because of Dunn's initials and Alstott's number,

along with the fact that they greased the wheels of Tampa Bay's running game.

6. When Tampa Bay began to pursue legendary quarterback Tom Brady during Brady's free agency in 2020, Bucs director of player personnel John Spytek came up with the front office's nickname for their (eventually successful) campaign: "Operation Shoeless Joe Jackson." Like the namesake player in the movie *Field of Dreams*, Spytek believed that the struggling Buccaneers franchise needed an unlikely savior to suddenly appear out of a cornfield.

7. Buccaneers owner Malcolm Glazer was often called "The Leprechaun" by the press, because he was a short man with a red beard who was frequently lucky in business.

8. Legend has it that that star Tampa Bay linebacker Derrick Brooks got his nickname "The Sheriff" from teammate Warren Sapp, after Sapp watched Brooks slow down speedy Atlanta Falcons quarterback Michael Vick and "force him to go the speed limit."

9. The "Gronk Spike" is one the NFL's most well-known touchdown celebrations. The Bucs tight end uses his arm to fire the football incredibly hard into the ground; it has been calculated that the ball travels at about 60 miles per hour and hits the ground with 650 pounds of force.

10. Current Tampa Bay nose tackle Vita Vea is almost universally known as Vita because his real full name is quite the mouthful: Tevita Tuli'aki'ono Tuipuloto Mosese Va'hae Fehoko Faletau Vea.

CHAPTER 4:

THE QUARTERBACKS

QUIZ TIME!

1. Which of these Buccaneers quarterbacks has been sacked by opponents the most times during the span of their career in Tampa (197 times)?

   a. Vinny Testaverde
   b. Steve DeBerg
   c. Jameis Winston
   d. Trent Dilfer

2. Jameis Winston holds the top four spots on the Buccaneers' all-time list of most passing touchdowns thrown in a season.

   a. True
   b. False

3. Which quarterback has thrown over 100 picks; the most intercepted passes in Tampa Bay Buccaneers franchise history?

   a. Jameis Winston
   b. Doug Williams

c. Josh Freeman

d. Vinny Testaverde

4. Who is the Tampa Bay Buccaneers all-time career leader in most passing yards, with just a shade under 20,000?

   a. Brad Johnson

   b. Vinny Testaverde

   c. Jameis Winston

   d. Steve DeBerg

5. Which Buccaneers player set the franchise record for most passing yards in a season by a Tampa Bay quarterback with 5,109; the only one ever to crack 5,000?

   a. Tom Brady

   b. Jameis Winston

   c. Doug Williams

   d. Vinny Testaverde

6. How many players that have played quarterback for the Buccaneers have been elected to the Pro Football Hall of Fame?

   a. 1: Steve Young

   b. 2: Steve Young and Tom Brady

   c. 3: Steve Young, Doug Williams, and Vinny Testaverde

   d. 5: Steve Young, Tom Brady, Doug Williams, Vinny Testaverde, and Steve Spurrier

7. Trent Dilfer has played more games at quarterback for the Buccaneers than any other player.

   a. True

   b. False

8. One journeyman Buccaneers quarterback has been a part of 13 NFL teams, more than any other franchise leader. Who was this well-travelled player?

   a. Vinny Testaverde
   b. Josh Freeman
   c. Josh Johnson
   d. Josh McCown

9. Which two Bucs were the youngest players in the team's history to start at quarterback at just 21 years old?

   a. Trent Dilfer and Shaun King
   b. Doug Williams and Craig Erickson
   c. Josh Freeman and Jameis Winston
   d. Mike Glennon and Chris Simms

10. Which Tampa Bay quarterback was moved to the Kansas City Chiefs to make way for Vinny Testaverde after the Buccaneers took Testaverde 1st overall in the 1987 NFL Draft?

    a. Steve Young
    b. Steve DeBerg
    c. Trent Dilfer
    d. Doug Williams

11. How old was Buccaneers legend Vinny Testaverde when he retired from his playing days in the NFL in 2007?

    a. 35 years old
    b. 38 years old
    c. 41 years old
    d. 44 years old

12. Buccaneers quarterback Steve DeBerg named previous quarterback Doug Williams as the godfather when his daughter Stacey was born in 1986.

    a. True
    b. False

13. The highest quarterback rating put up by a Tampa Bay Buccaneer for a full season was 72.5. Which quarterback scored this franchise high mark?

    a. Vinny Testaverde
    b. Jeff Garcia
    c. Josh Johnson
    d. Tom Brady

14. Which risk-averse Bucs quarterback tossed only six interceptions while starting 16 games for the squad over the course of a regular season, easily setting the franchise record?

    a. Trent Dilfer
    b. Brian Griese
    c. Josh Freeman
    d. Tom Brady

15. Buccaneers leader Steve Young holds the franchise's record for most rushing yards in a season by a quarterback, which he set in 1986. How many yards did he rack up?

    a. 425
    b. 603

c. 729

d. 904

16. Tampa Bay quarterback Trent Dilfer has won a high school football state championship, a college football National Championship, and a Super Bowl.

    a. True

    b. False

17. Which of the following is NOT true about Buccaneers quarterback Vinny Testaverde?

    a. He has more passing yards and more touchdown passes than any quarterbacks who are eligible but have not been inducted into the Pro Football Hall of Fame.

    b. He has the Tampa Bay record for most game-winning drives in a single season.

    c. He has completed an NFL pass to more players than any other quarterback.

    d. He has more losses as a starting quarterback than any other player in NFL history.

18. Which two Tampa Bay quarterbacks have led the team to the most fourth quarter comeback victories in a single season, with each putting up five such wins?

    a. Vinny Testaverde and Tom Brady

    b. Trent Dilfer and Jameis Winston

    c. Steve Young and Brad Johnson

    d. Doug Williams and Josh Freeman

19. How many times did prolific Buccaneers quarterback Jameis Winston throw for 20 (or more) touchdowns in a single season?

    a. 1

    b. 3

    c. 4

    d. 6

20. Among quarterbacks who have started at least five games with Tampa Bay, Gary Huff has the highest interception percentage, with 9.2% of his passes thrown being picked off.

    a. True

    b. False

QUIZ ANSWERS

1. A – Vinny Testaverde
2. B – False
3. D – Vinny Testaverde
4. C – Jameis Winston
5. B – Jameis Winston
6. A – 1: Steve Young
7. A – True
8. C – Josh Johnson
9. C – Josh Freeman and Jameis Winston
10. B – Steve DeBerg
11. D – 44 years old
12. B – False
13. D – Tom Brady
14. C – Josh Freeman
15. A – 425
16. B – False
17. B – He has the Tampa Bay record for most game-winning drives in a single season.
18. D – Doug Williams and Josh Freeman
19. B – 3
20. A – True

DID YOU KNOW?

1. Quarterback Josh Freeman owns the longest passing play in Buccaneers history. He dropped back and found talented receiver Vincent Jackson for a 95-yard touchdown toss against the New Orleans Saints in 2012 that still stands as the team's benchmark.

2. No Buccaneers starting quarterback has ever been able to complete 70% of his passes in a season. The most accurate field general was Brian Griese, who came the closest in 2004 when he hit 69.3%.

3. At many points in their history, the Buccaneers could have used some better blocking. Three times, and with three different quarterbacks, the team allowed a single quarterback to be sacked 47 times during a single season. Steve Young was sacked that often when he dropped back to pass in 1986, Trent Dilfer went down just as many times in 1995, and Jameis Winston matched the total again in 2019.

4. Only one Buccaneers quarterback has played his entire NFL career with Tampa Bay. Interestingly, this was Parnell Dickinson, who started at quarterback for the team during their very first year in the NFL, 1976. However, that was also Dickinson's *only* season with the team, as an injury ended his career before it got far off the ground.

5. Steve DeBerg, Vinny Testaverde, and Trent Dilfer have served the longest tenure as the starting quarterback for the Buccaneers. Each of the three started for at least part of six different seasons, which no Tampa Bay starter has lasted beyond.

6. In Tom Brady's one season (2020) in Tampa Bay, he re-wrote the team's record books. No quarterback had ever completed more than 380 passes before, yet Brady broke the 400-completion plateau. None had thrown for over 33 touchdowns; Brady put up 40. No one had achieved a quarterback rating of higher than 70 before; Brady recorded a 72.5.

7. Quarterback Vinny Testaverde spent an incredible 21 seasons as an NFL player, including his first six years in Tampa Bay from 1987 to 1992. Thanks to this longevity, Testaverde holds a dubious NFL record: most losses while holding the starting quarterback job. Testaverde was on the losing end 123 times during his career.

8. In 2009, former Tampa Bay quarterback Doug Williams partnered with ex-Bills, Rams, and Chargers quarterback James Harris to form the Black College Football Hall of Fame. Harris and Williams had both been stars at Grambling State University, a historically black university that later named a street in Williams's honor.

9. Tampa Bay quarterback Jeff Garcia was inspired to work hard and become a successful football player to make his parents proud. The Garcia family had been tragically

affected by the death of Jeff's twin sisters, the drowning death of his brother, and the passing of another sister who was killed in a vehicle accident.

10. When the Bucs brought in free agent quarterback Tom Brady in 2020, he led them to the Super Bowl. But along the way there was one minor hiccup: during a nail-biting 20-19 loss to the Chicago Bears, Brady forgot what down it was at the end of the game. After tossing an incompletion on the fourth down to seal Tampa Bay's fate, Brady held up four fingers, mistakenly exhorting his teammates to get back to the line of scrimmage for what he believed was another chance to keep the drive alive before being told that was not the case.

CHAPTER 5:

THE PASS CATCHERS

QUIZ TIME!

1. Five wide receivers have recorded over 25 career touchdown catches for the Buccaneers. Which one of them has the most scores?

   a. Joey Galloway
   b. Mike Williams
   c. Mike Evans
   d. Kevin House

2. No one in Buccaneers history is within 100 receptions of wide receiver Mike Evans at the top of Tampa Bay's record book.

   a. True
   b. False

3. Who is the Buccaneers' single-season leader in receiving touchdowns scored, with 13?

   a. Tight end Rob Gronkowski
   b. Wide receiver Mike Evans

    c. Tight end Cameron Brate

    d. Wide receiver Joey Galloway

4. Who holds the all-time career franchise record for most receiving yardage for the Buccaneers?

    a. Wide receiver Keyshawn Johnson

    b. Tight end Jimmie Giles

    c. Wide receiver Mark Carrier

    d. Wide receiver Mike Evans

5. How many receiving yards did Bucs franchise wide receiver Mike Evans pick up when he debuted for the team as a rookie in 2014 against the Carolina Panthers?

    a. 37

    b. 89

    c. 142

    d. 177

6. No Buccaneers with at least 100 receptions has averaged 20 yards per catch over their careers. Who showed the team's most consistent big play ability by averaging 17.8 yards per catch?

    a. Wide receiver Kevin House

    b. Tight end O.J. Howard

    c. Wide receiver Joey Galloway

    d. Wide receiver Morris Owens

7. Tampa Bay's Mike Evans became the youngest wide receiver to record 200 receiving yards in a single game, after posting 209 yards against Washington in 2014 at the age of 21.

a. True

b. False

8. Which Buccaneers pass catcher has played more NFL games with the franchise than any other player?

   a. Tight end Jimmie Giles

   b. Wide receiver Mike Evans

   c. Tight end Dave Moore

   d. Wide receiver Gerald Carter

9. Five pass catchers have over 300 career receptions for the Tampa Bay Buccaneers. Which of the following players is NOT among that club?

   a. Running back James Wilder

   b. Wide receiver Keyshawn Johnson

   c. Running back Warrick Dunn

   d. Fullback Mike Alstott

10. Tampa Bay wide receivers have been pretty sure-handed over the years, but two players lead the position with eight career fumbles apiece for the Bucs. Which two players coughed up the ball most often?

    a. Mark Carrier and Michael Clayton

    b. Adam Humphries and Chris Godwin

    c. Jacquez Green and Kevin House

    d. Ike Hilliard and Preston Parker

11. At the end of the 2020 NFL season, the Buccaneers had a stable of excellent pass catchers under contract for 2021.

Which one of those has the highest base salary for the year at almost $16 million?

a. Wide receiver Chris Godwin

b. Tight end Rob Gronkowski

c. Wide receiver Mike Evans

d. Wide receiver Antonio Brown

12. Speedy Tampa Bay Buccaneers wide receiver DeSean Jackson once participated in an unusual race in which he competed in a 40-yard dash against a racehorse and a motorcycle. Jackson defeated the horse but finished behind the motorcycle.

a. True

b. False

13. How many Buccaneers tight ends have caught over 200 passes for the club during their careers?

a. 1: Jimmie Giles

b. 2: Jimmie Giles and Cameron Brate

c. 3: Jimmie Giles, Cameron Brate, and Kellen Winslow

d. 4: Jimmie Giles, Cameron Brate, Kellen Winslow, and Ron Hall

14. Which two teammates posted the highest combined receiving yardage total in a season for the Buccaneers, with 2,490 altogether?

a. Wide receiver Antonio Bryant and tight end Kellen Winslow in 2009

b. Wide receivers Chris Godwin and Mike Evans in 2019

c. Wide receiver Kevin House and tight end Jimmie Giles in 1983

d. Wide receivers Vincent Jackson and Mike Williams in 2013

15. Which of the following circumstances contributing to his difficult childhood was NOT actually faced and overcome by Buccaneers wide receiver Mike Evans?

   a. He was born when his mother, Heather, was only 14 years old.

   b. His twin brother, David, passed away in a drowning accident when the two boys were six years old.

   c. His father, Mickey, was physically abusive toward the family.

   d. His uncle shot and killed his father after Evans turned 9 years old.

16. The Buccaneers played three tight ends in their 2020 Super Bowl victory over the Kansas City Chiefs, but only O.J. Howard recorded a touchdown in the matchup.

   a. True

   b. False

17. Only three players in NFL history have started their careers with five straight seasons recording over 1,000 yards receiving. Tampa Bay's Mike Evans is one; but which other two superstars did he join?

   a. Randy Moss of the Minnesota Vikings and A.J. Green of the Cincinnati Bengals

b. Jerry Rice of the San Francisco 49ers and Sterling Sharpe of the Green Bay Packers

c. Steve Largent of the Seattle Seahawks and Julio Jones of the Atlanta Falcons

d. Art Monk of the Washington Redskins and Calvin Johnson of the Detroit Lions

18. Which Buccaneer recorded the most catches in one season for the team, when he hauled in 106 passes for the squad and became the only Buc to break the century mark?

a. Tight end Kellen Winslow in 2009

b. Wide receiver Mike Evans in 2016

c. Wide receiver Keyshawn Johnson in 2001

d. Wide receiver Keenan McCardell in 2003

19. Which Buccaneer twice partnered with a teammate to record 20 combined touchdown receptions in a single season?

a. Cameron Brate

b. Vincent Jackson

c. Chris Godwin

d. Mike Evans

20. Tampa Bay wide receiver Mike Evans once played a game against the Denver Broncos in which he caught only two passes, for only two yards, but both catches were touchdowns for the Buccaneers.

a. True

b. False

QUIZ ANSWERS

1. C – Mike Evans

2. A – True

3. B – Wide receiver Mike Evans

4. D – Wide receiver Mike Evans

5. A – 37

6. D – Wide receiver Morris Owens

7. A – True

8. C – Tight end Dave Moore

9. B – Wide receiver Keyshawn Johnson

10. D – Ike Hilliard and Preston Parker

11. A – Wide receiver Chris Godwin

12. B – False

13. D – 4: Jimmie Giles, Cameron Brate, Kellen Winslow, and Ron Hall

14. B – Wide receivers Chris Godwin and Mike Evans in 2019

15. B – His twin brother, David, passed away in a drowning accident when the two boys were six years old.

16. B – False

17. A – Randy Moss of the Minnesota Vikings and A.J. Green of the Cincinnati Bengals

18. C – Wide receiver Keyshawn Johnson in 2001

19. D – Mike Evans

20. A – True

DID YOU KNOW?

1. Legendary wide receiver Tim Brown ranks seventh on the all-time list for most receiving yards in NFL history. Brown finished his career with Tampa Bay in 2004 and sits sandwiched between tight end Tony Gonzalez and wide receiver Steve Smith on the list.

2. The single-game record for most receiving yards in Tampa Bay Buccaneers history was actually set in 2012 by wide receiver Vincent Jackson against the New Orleans Saints. Jackson reeled in 216 yards that day to eclipse the 212 that receiver Mark Carrier had set as the benchmark a quarter century previously.

3. During his decade-long NFL career, Bucs tight end Rob Gronkowski has earned $54 million from his playing contracts, and has not spent a cent of it. The popular Gronkowski has instead saved every penny, living off of the endorsement money he makes from his numerous non-football ventures.

4. Only 19 tight ends in NFL history have recorded more than 500 pass receptions. The Buccaneers boast one of those tight ends: Rob Gronkowski, who has 566 catches, though the majority came while he was playing for the New England Patriots.

5. In 1983, tight end Jimmie Giles staged the first-ever contract holdout by a Buccaneers player and missed

training camp in a dispute over his salary. No animosity lingered afterward though, as the team kept Giles for years afterward and eventually inducted him into the Tampa Bay Buccaneers' Ring of Honor.

6. Tampa Bay tight end Jimmie Giles holds the team record for most receiving touchdowns in a single game, with four. This is just one off of the NFL's overall record. Giles went off against the Miami Dolphins in 1985, hauling in scoring passes of seven, 15, 16, and 39 yards from Bucs quarterback Steve DeBerg that day.

7. Bucs wide receiver Keyshawn Johnson was not shy about his desires. The outspoken Johnson was frequently relied upon by media members for colorful quotes, and no one was surprised when he titled his autobiography *Just Give Me the Damn Ball.*

8. Because wide receiver Vincent Jackson's parents were both in the United States military, Jackson provided tickets for families of armed forces members at every Tampa Bay home game after he joined the team.

9. After seven seasons with the Buccaneers, wide receiver Kevin House played one year with the Los Angeles Rams and then gave up the NFL for a new profession: hairdressing. House started up a hair salon and ran it for a decade, helping other Tampa Bay customers like linebacker Hardy Nickerson and coach Tony Dungy look their best.

10. High praise has always followed Tampa Bay tight end Rob Gronkowski around. As one of the greatest tight ends

in NFL history, Gronkowski has been variously described as "a generational marvel," "the gold standard," "an on-field force of nature," and "an NFL Supernova."

CHAPTER 6:

RUNNING WILD

QUIZ TIME!

1. Who holds the Buccaneers' single-season franchise rushing yardage record after racking up 1,544 yards on the ground; the only player to crack 1,500?

    a. Doug Martin
    b. James Wilder
    c. Cadillac Williams
    d. Warrick Dunn

2. It is a Buccaneers tradition for every running back to tap his helmet against the helmets of the starting offensive linemen before a game. This must happen following the warm-up but before the national anthem is sung.

    a. True
    b. False

3. Which running back has accumulated the most carries for Tampa Bay without ever scoring even a single rushing touchdown (90)?

a. Charles Sims

b. William Howard

c. Mel Carver

d. Ron Springs

4. Which of the following is NOT true about talented Buccaneers running back Warrick Dunn?

a. He started a charity program called Homes For The Holidays, which gave homes to needy families, including one to the family of future NFL superstar Deshaun Watson.

b. He became a minority owner of the Atlanta Falcons after his playing career ended.

c. He retired as the Buccaneers all-time leading rusher in 2008, but has since been passed.

d. He published an autobiography detailing his struggles with mental health, called *Running for My Life*.

5. How many running backs have been handed the ball over 1,000 times for the Buccaneers?

a. 1: James Wilder

b. 2: James Wilder and Mike Alstott

c. 3: James Wilder, Mike Alstott, and Warrick Dunn

d. 4: James Wilder, Mike Alstott, Warrick Dunn, and Doug Martin

6. No Bucs running back with at least 30 games played has averaged over 100 yards per game during his career. Doug Martin is the closest; what is his average?

a. 68.1

b. 73.4

c. 81.7

d. 95.2

7. Mike Alstott has 58 rushing touchdowns with the Buccaneers, which is more than the next two highest Tampa Bay running backs combined.

a. True

b. False

8. In which season did Doug Martin record an astonishing 4.9 yards per carry for Tampa Bay?

a. 2013

b. 2014

c. 2015

d. 2017

9. Which Tampa Bay running back (with at least 300 carries) has the highest yards gained per attempt, with 4.6 over the course of his career?

a. Ronald Jones II

b. Michael Pittman

c. Earnest Graham

d. LeGarrette Blount

10. Buccaneers running back Doug Martin recorded his first NFL touchdown against which NFL team?

a. New York Giants

b. New Orleans Saints

c. New England Patriots

d. New York Jets

11. How many different players appear in the Buccaneers' list of top 10 most rushing touchdowns in a single season?

    a. 3

    b. 5

    c. 8

    d. 10

12. Bucs running back Ricky Bell was the brother of a famous R&B singer Archie Bell of the group Archie Bell and the Drells. However, Bell is of no relation to the R&B singer of the same name, Ricky Bell, who founded groups called New Edition and Bell Biv DeVoe.

    a. True

    b. False

13. Which Tampa Bay running back has committed the most career fumbles, with 44?

    a. James Wilder

    b. Mike Alstott

    c. Michael Pittman

    d. Ricky Bell

14. Which Buccaneer had the highest single-season rushing yards per game, nearly reaching the century mark with 96.5?

    a. Doug Martin

    b. Errict Rhett

   c. LeGarrette Blount

   d. James Wilder

15. Beloved Bucs fullback Mike Alstott was ultimately forced to retire after 11 seasons in Tampa due to an injury to which part of his body?

   a. Back

   b. Neck

   c. Leg

   d. Eye

16. Before joining the Buccaneers, running back LeGarrette Blount was suspended for most of a season in the NCAA after sucker punching an opponent who taunted Blount after his team lost a game.

   a. True

   b. False

17. Bucs running back Earnest Graham ended his career after he suffered an Achilles injury during an NFL game played in which city?

   a. Tampa Bay, Florida

   b. Chicago, Illinois

   c. London, England

   d. Mexico City, Mexico

18. The life of Buccaneers running back Ricky Bell, who died at the young age of 29 from a skin and muscle disorder, was made into a movie that featured which Hollywood star in the role of Bell?

a. Omar Epps

b. Samuel L. Jackson

c. Wesley Snipes

d. Mario Van Peebles

19. After retiring from football, Buccaneers running back Cadillac Williams became a running backs coach in all of the following places, except for which one?

a. NCAA for the Auburn Tigers

b. Alliance of American Football for the Birmingham Iron

c. NFL for the Tampa Bay Buccaneers

d. IMG Academy for the White Team

20. Tampa Bay running back Leonard Fournette holds the NFL record as the youngest player to score a rushing touchdown that was at least 90 yards long.

a. True

b. False

QUIZ ANSWERS

1. B – James Wilder

2. B – False

3. D – Ron Springs

4. C – He retired as the Buccaneers all-time leading rusher in 2008, but has since been passed.

5. D – 4: James Wilder, Mike Alstott, Warrick Dunn, and Doug Martin

6. A – 68.1

7. B – False

8. C – 2015

9. D – LeGarrette Blount

10. A – New York Giants

11. C – 8

12. A – True

13. A – James Wilder

14. D – James Wilder

15. B – Neck

16. A – True

17. C – London, England

18. D – Mario Van Peebles

19. C – NFL for the Tampa Bay Buccaneers

20. A – True

DID YOU KNOW?

1. No running backs who have played for the Buccaneers have been enshrined in the Pro Football Hall of Fame. This is the team's only position group without at least one player selected.

2. Tampa Bay's Warrick Dunn had a philanthropic streak that was recognized well outside the NFL community. In fact, United States President Bill Clinton even presented Dunn with a Giant Steps Award for his notable accomplishments in civic leadership.

3. Eleven times in NFL history, a running back has scored 20 or more rushing touchdowns in a single season. No Tampa Bay back has really gotten close to the mark, as James Wilder is the closest with just 13 touchdowns scored.

4. In 2009, Tampa Bay running back Cadillac Williams returned to the field after a series of knee injuries and finished second in the Comeback Player of the Year Award voting. He was bested for the award by a future Buccaneer: then-New England Patriots quarterback Tom Brady.

5. Bucs running back Peyton Barber made it to college despite suffering from both ADHD and dyslexia during his childhood. Barber did not graduate from Auburn

University, but only because he left two years early to enter the NFL Draft.

6. Despite playing for Tampa Bay seven years after their first Super Bowl win, and the Pittsburgh Steelers five years after they took home a title, running back LeGarrette Blount still got his timing right by becoming one of just six players in history to win back-to-back Super Bowls with two different franchises (the New England Patriots and Philadelphia Eagles, in Blount's case).

7. In 1990, the Bucs took a chance on running back Reggie Cobb in the NFL Draft. Just three months earlier, Cobb had entered a rehab facility to fight his drug addiction. His talent won out though, and Cobb did spend four relatively successful seasons with the team.

8. Tampa Bay running back Michael Pittman was a proud father when his son, Michael Pittman Jr., also earned his way into the NFL. The younger Pittman is a wide receiver who was drafted by the Indianapolis Colts in 2020.

9. In 1984, Tampa Bay running back James Wilder was just 16 yards shy of the NFL record for most combined rushing and receiving yards. During the last game of the year, Bucs coach John McKay even ordered the defense to allow the other team to score in the fourth quarter so Tampa Bay could get the ball back and try to help Wilder break the record. The team stood still and gave up a touchdown, but the plan didn't work as Wilder gained no further yards, and McKay was later fined by the NFL.

10. The mother of popular Buccaneers running back Warrick Dunn was murdered in 1993 by armed robbers. Dunn later met one of the killers responsible, who had been sentenced to death, and forgave the man.

CHAPTER 7:

IN THE TRENCHES

QUIZ TIME!

1. Three Buccaneers defenders have recorded four sacks in a single game, which is tops for the franchise. Which three were they?

    a. Defensive end Jason Pierre-Paul and defensive tackles Warren Sapp and Gerald McCoy

    b. Defensive end Chidi Ahanotu, linebacker Lavonte David, and cornerback Ronde Barber

    c. Linebacker Shaquil Barrett and defensive ends Simeon Rice and Marcus Jones

    d. Defensive ends Stylez White, Lee Roy Selmon, and William Gholston

2. The 2016 Tampa Bay Buccaneers hold the NFL record for the heaviest combined weight of all starting offensive and defensive linemen, having been measured officially on opening day at 3,281 pounds.

    a. True

    b. False

3. Who is the Buccaneers' all-time franchise leader in sacks (since the sack became an official stat), having taken down opposing quarterbacks 78.5 times?

   a. Defensive end Simeon Rice
   b. Defensive tackle Gerald McCoy
   c. Defensive end Jason Pierre-Paul
   d. Defensive end Lee Roy Selmon

4. Which offensive lineman did the Bucs select highest in the NFL Entry Draft, using a 4th overall selection to add the stout blocker to their team?

   a. Left tackle Paul Gruber
   b. Right tackle Charles McCrae
   c. Guard Sean Farrell
   d. Right tackle Tristan Wirfs

5. Which offensive lineman has played more games on the offensive side of the Buccaneers' line of scrimmage than anyone else?

   a. Center Tony Mayberry
   b. Guard Ian Beckles
   c. Tackle Paul Gruber
   d. Tackle Demar Dotson

6. Which defensive lineman has played more games on the defensive side of the Buccaneers' line of scrimmage than anyone else?

   a. Tackle Warren Sapp
   b. End John Cannon

c. Tackle Gerald McCoy

d. End Chidi Ahanotu

7. Former Buccaneers defensive tackle Dave Pear suffered through back surgery, hip replacement, loss of memory, slurred speech, and vertigo as a result of his playing days, and remarked to reporters, "Don't let your kids play football. Never."

a. True

b. False

8. Two Buccaneers defenders showed the best nose for the ball by leading the team in most career forced fumbles, with 24. Which two players caused these fumbles?

a. Defensive ends Simeon Rice and Eric Curry

b. Cornerbacks Ronde Barber and Ricky Reynolds

c. Safeties John Lynch and Jermaine Phillips

d. Linebackers Derrick Brooks and Lavonte David

9. Quarterbacks top the record books for most fumbles recovered for the Buccaneers, but they tend to be cleaning up their own mess. Which defender has created the most turnovers for Tampa Bay by scooping up an opponent's fumble?

a. Defensive end Lee Roy Selmon

b. Linebacker Lavonte David

c. Cornerback Ronde Barber

d. Defensive tackle Warren Sapp

10. Which Tampa Bay Buccaneer once maintained his own website, which was called qbkilla.com?

   a. Linebacker Devin White
   b. Defensive tackle Warren Sapp
   c. Defensive end Simeon Rice
   d. Linebacker Broderick Thomas

11. Buccaneers mainstay Demar Dotson played 130 NFL games as an offensive tackle with the club. Where does he rank in all-time games played for Tampa Bay?

   a. 3rd overall
   b. Tied for 7th overall
   c. 10th overall
   d. Tied for 12th overall

12. Former Tampa Bay center Randy Grimes became a counselor at the same rehab center he attended in order to shed an addiction to painkillers that he was given while playing in the NFL.

   a. True
   b. False

13. Which current Buccaneers defensive lineman has the longest tenure in Tampa Bay?

   a. Defensive tackle Ndamukong Suh
   b. Nose tackle Vita Vea
   c. Defensive end William Gholston
   d. Nose tackle Steve McClendon

14. Which of the following facts about Bucs defensive lineman Brad Culpepper is NOT true?

   a. He competed on two seasons of the popular reality television show *Survivor*, including one in which he finished in second place.
   b. He was an early investor in the Starbucks coffee chain and owns over two dozen franchises.
   c. He was an Academic All-American who once won an award as the best student-athlete in the NCAA.
   d. He argued courtroom cases as a trial lawyer after finishing his football career.

15. While broadcasting for *Monday Night Football*, former Bucs defensive tackle Anthony McFarland was often stationed not in the broadcast booth, but remotely, in a crane called "The Booger Mobile."

   a. True
   b. False

16. In 2019, Bucs nose tackle Vita Vea caught a touchdown pass thrown by quarterback Jameis Winston, allowing the 347-pound Vea to set the NFL record as the heaviest player of all time to record a receiving touchdown.

   a. True
   b. False

17. Before a couple of games in the 2002 and 2003 NFL seasons, Tampa Bay defensive tackle Warren Sapp stirred up controversy by doing what unusual activity?

a. Skipping through the members of the opposing team during their warm-up on the field

b. Catching and flipping the ceremonial coin used for the coin toss while it was rotating in mid air

c. Kneeling during the singing of the national anthem as a form of protest

d. Stating to reporters that his intention was to "knock (somebody) out of the game, hopefully for the rest of the season"

18. About which Tampa Bay defensive lineman did a Detroit Lions coach once remark "(he's) a grown man at work among a bunch of boys"?

a. Tackle Warren Sapp

b. End Lee Roy Selmon

c. Tackle Vita Vea

d. Tackle Ndamukong Suh

19. Which of the following pop culture appearances was NOT made by Buccaneers Hall of Fame defensive tackle Warren Sapp after his playing career ended?

a. Comedian at a roast of celebrity Larry the Cable Guy

b. Contestant on the television show *Dancing with the Stars*

c. Rapper with a guest verse on the album of superstar rapper Pitbull

d. Judge on the television show *BBQ Pitmasters*

20. Buccaneers defensive end Stylez White is a self-described "adrenaline junkie" who requested (and received) a

clause in his contract allowing him to participate in activities such as bungee jumping, skydiving, and motorcycle racing. White was forced to stipulate that the Bucs would not be liable to pay him if he suffered an injury during any of those activities.

a. True
b. False

QUIZ ANSWERS

1. C – Linebacker Shaquil Barrett and defensive ends Simeon Rice and Marcus Jones

2. B – False

3. D – Defensive end Lee Roy Selmon

4. A – Left tackle Paul Gruber

5. C – Tackle Paul Gruber

6. A – Tackle Warren Sapp

7. A – True

8. D – Linebackers Derrick Brooks and Lavonte David

9. B – Linebacker Lavonte David

10. B – Defensive tackle Warren Sapp

11. D – Tied for 12th overall

12. A – True

13. C – Defensive end William Gholston

14. B – He was an early investor in the Starbucks coffee chain and owns over two dozen franchises.

15. A – True

16. A – True

17. A – Skipping through the members of the opposing team during their warm-up on the field

18. B – End Lee Roy Selmon

19. C – Rapper with a guest verse on the album of superstar rapper Pitbull

20. B – False

DID YOU KNOW?

1. Eight defensive players share the Tampa Bay record for most safeties created, as no one in franchise history has been responsible for more than one. However, they are joined by one offensive player, running back Kerry Goode, who also recorded one during his time with the Bucs.

2. After finishing his career with the Tampa Bay Buccaneers, defensive end Marcus Jones switched to another violent, physical career. Jones became a mixed martial artist nicknamed "The Darkness" and even appeared on the popular television show *The Ultimate Fighter* in 2009.

3. Bucs defensive tackle Warren Sapp always played on the edge as a very hard hitter. Even before reaching college or the NFL, in high school Sapp once tackled future Major League Baseball star Johnny Damon so violently that Damon was concussed.

4. In retirement, Tampa Bay defensive end Simeon Rice became an entertainment mogul who formed his own hip-hop label, Lucid Dream Entertainment, and then went on to direct films including *When I Was King* and *Unsullied*.

5. Only one Bucs player started for the team in each season during Tampa Bay's first decade of existence. Center Steve Wilson did so for the team from 1976 to 1985,

including 1979 when the offensive line allowed just a dozen sacks all season.

6. Bucs offensive tackle Rob Taylor joined the team in an unusual fashion. Four years after becoming a 12th round draft pick of the Philadelphia Eagles, Taylor had never played a single game and was out of the NFL and playing in the USFL. On a vacation to Tampa Bay with his spouse, Taylor stopped by the Buccaneers' headquarters, asked for a tryout, was amazingly given one, then signed with the team and stayed for eight years.

7. Offensive guard George Yarno scored one point in his eight-year career with the Bucs. In 1983, Yarno was brought in to convert a point after attempt as the team's emergency kicker, and easily booted the ball between the uprights.

8. After retirement from his playing career, longtime Buccaneers guard Ian Beckles stayed in Tampa Bay and became a publisher. Beckles was also the editor-in-chief of a magazine called *What's Hot Tampa Bay*.

9. Defensive end William Gholston and his cousin, defensive end Vernon Gholston, both made it to the NFL. In a twist of fate, Vernon was drafted 6th overall by the New York Jets in 2008, but made only five NFL starts, while William was the less heralded pick at 126th overall in 2013 but has started 68 games and counting for the Bucs.

10. As of 2021, the NFL's active leader in most consecutive games started was Tampa Bay defensive tackle Ndamukong

Suh with 147. Suh's ironman streak began with the Detroit Lions, and he maintained it with the Miami Dolphins and Los Angeles Rams before continuing it in Tampa.

CHAPTER 8:

THE BACK SEVEN

QUIZ TIME!

1. Which Buccaneers cornerback is the franchise's all-time leader in interceptions, with 47?

   a. Cornerback Ronde Barber
   b. Free safety Cedrick Brown
   c. Cornerback Donnie Abraham
   d. Strong safety John Lynch

2. During the 2010s poker craze, members of Tampa Bay's secondary and linebacking corps held a weekly game where, rather than playing for money, the losers had to tweet embarrassing things about themselves or flattering things about the winners.

   a. True
   b. False

3. Which Buccaneers player has the team's lead for most interceptions returned for a touchdown, with eight scores accomplished in this manner?

a. Linebacker Derrick Brooks

b. Cornerback Aqib Talib

c. Safety Tanard Jackson

d. Cornerback Ronde Barber

4. Although sacks are usually not a high priority for defensive backs in most coaching systems, one Bucs defensive back excelled at this skill, putting up 28 sacks in his career. Who?

a. Strong safety John Lynch

b. Free safety Harry Hamilton

c. Cornerback Ronde Barber

d. Cornerback Brian Kelly

5. The initials in popular Buccaneers cornerback E.J. Biggers's name actually come from his real name, which is which of the following?

a. Edward Joseph

b. Eric James

c. Edjaun Cinclair

d. Emilio Jr.

6. Which Tampa Bay linebacker was so intelligent that just a few games into his rookie season, he was given the one helmet allowed on defense, marked with a green circle, that contained a radio transmitter through which the coaches relayed plays onto the field?

a. Derrick Brooks

b. Devin White

    c. Hardy Nickerson

    d. Lavonte David

7. Tampa Bay cornerback Brian Kelly went to the University of Southern California as a player but would go on to become the head coach of their rivals, the Notre Dame Fighting Irish, after retiring from the NFL.

    a. True

    b. False

8. Which of the following players is NOT one of the three Buccaneers in history who have scored touchdowns on a fumble recovery and an interception during the same season?

    a. Cornerback Ronde Barber

    b. Linebacker Richard Wood

    c. Linebacker Derrick Brooks

    d. Safety John Lynch

9. Cornerback Ronde Barber played his entire NFL career with the Tampa Bay Buccaneers after they picked him in the 3rd round in 1997. How long did that career last?

    a. 12 seasons

    b. 14 seasons

    c. 16 seasons

    d. 19 seasons

10. Tampa Bay linebacker Derrick Brooks was selected for 11 Pro Bowls during his career. Only two NFL linebackers have ever been to more; which two?

a. Jack Lambert of Pittsburgh Steelers and Brian Urlacher of the Chicago Bears

b. Ray Lewis of the Baltimore Ravens and Junior Seau of the San Diego Chargers

c. Dick Butkus of the Chicago Bears and Derrick Thomas of the Kansas City Chiefs

d. Ray Nitschke of the Green Bay Packers and Bobby Wagner of the Seattle Seahawks

11. Buccaneers mainstay Shelton Quarles played almost 150 NFL games as a linebacker with the club. Where does he rank in games played all-time for Tampa Bay?

a. 2nd overall

b. Tied for 4th overall

c. 5th overall

d. 8th overall

12. Years after his NFL playing career was over, Tampa Bay linebacker Derrick Brooks became the president and part owner of an Arena League Football team called the Tampa Bay Storm.

a. True

b. False

13. With which of the following teams has Hall of Fame Buccaneers safety John Lynch become a general manager after retiring from his playing and broadcasting careers?

a. New England Patriots

b. San Francisco 49ers

c. Denver Broncos

d. Tampa Bay Buccaneers

14. Which of these current Buccaneers linebackers has been with the team for nine seasons; the longest current tenure in Tampa Bay's back seven?

a. Kevin Minter

b. Shaquil Barrett

c. Lavonte David

d. Jason Pierre-Paul

15. Which of the following Buccaneers records is NOT held by cornerback Ronde Barber?

a. Most career touchdowns by a defensive player: 14

b. Most sacks in a game: 3

c. Most interceptions in a season: 10

d. Most interceptions in a game: 3

16. In 1984, cornerback Mike Washington established the Shut Down Time tradition, wherein he donated his gold pocket watch upon retirement to the next cornerback to take up the mantle for Tampa Bay. To this day, the watch hangs in a cornerback's locker, and he must pass it on if he retires, is traded, cut, or signs elsewhere.

a. True

b. False

17. Which Tampa Bay defender has recorded the most tackles in a single season, after racking up 214 of them in 1993?

a. Linebacker Kwon Alexander

b. Linebacker Hardy Nickerson

c. Linebacker Lavonte David

d. Linebacker Derrick Brooks

18. Tampa Bay linebacker Derrick Brooks started 219 consecutive games (including playoffs) for the Bucs. This puts him second all-time in NFL history at the position, only two games behind only which other player?

a. Bill Romanowski

b. Ryan Kerrigan

c. London Fletcher

d. Lee Roy Jordan

19. Which of the following positions did Tampa Bay linebacker Hardy Nickerson NOT hold after his playing career was finished?

a. Radio broadcaster and analyst on Buccaneers Radio Network

b. Linebackers coach for three different NFL franchises

c. Head coach at Bishop O'Dowd High School in Oakland, California

d. Director of scouting for the Chicago Bears

20. Tampa Bay cornerback Ronde Barber has an identical twin brother named Tiki. The two played together at the University of Virginia before Tiki, a running back, was drafted by the New York Giants the same year the Buccaneers drafted Ronde.

a. True

b. False

QUIZ ANSWERS

1. A – Cornerback Ronde Barber
2. B – False
3. D – Cornerback Ronde Barber
4. C – Cornerback Ronde Barber
5. C – Edjaun Cinclair
6. D – Lavonte David
7. B – False
8. D – Safety John Lynch
9. C – 16 seasons
10. B – Ray Lewis of the Baltimore Ravens and Junior Seau of the San Diego Chargers
11. D – 8th overall
12. A – True
13. B – San Francisco 49ers
14. C – Lavonte David
15. B – Most sacks in a game: 3
16. B – False
17. B – Linebacker Hardy Nickerson
18. C – London Fletcher
19. D – Director of scouting for the Chicago Bears
20. A – True

DID YOU KNOW?

1. Passes defended is a stat that the NFL began using at the turn of the century. Cornerback Ronde Barber has dominated the statistic for the Buccaneers (197), having stopped almost 100 more than his closest competition, cornerback Brian Kelly (99).

2. Buccaneers cornerback Ronde Barber and his brother Tiki have written several children's books together. Most are football-themed, but they have also expanded into baseball and basketball books as well.

3. Linebacker Derrick Brooks is the all-time leading tackler for the Bucs franchise. Brooks played in Tampa Bay for 14 seasons and racked up 2,198 tackles during that time.

4. Only two NFL players have ever recorded 40 career interceptions and 20 career sacks. One is Hall of Fame defensive back Charles Woodson, and the other is the Buccaneers iconic cornerback, Ronde Barber, who had 47 picks and 28 sacks during his time in Tampa Bay.

5. The longest play in Buccaneers history is not held by any offensive player, but by Tampa Bay linebacker Shelton Quarles, who picked off a pass against the Green Bay Packers and raced for a 98-yard touchdown during the 2001 NFL season.

6. Mark Cotney was a safety on the inaugural Tampa Bay team in 1976 and lasted with the team through the 1984

season before being forced to retire due to an unfortunate tackle on running back Gerald Riggs which left Cotney with two damaged vertebrae.

7. One defensive back who has played for the Buccaneers has been enshrined in the Football Hall of Fame. This was safety John Lynch, who was elected in 2021.

8. Tampa Bay has also sent one linebacker to the Pro Football Hall of Fame: Derrick Brooks. Brooks got the nod in 2014 after over a decade spent with the Bucs.

9. Despite playing eleven seasons in Tampa Bay and just four in Denver, safety John Lynch was inducted into the Broncos Ring of Fame one month *before* he was selected for the Buccaneers Ring of Honor.

10. Tampa Bay cornerback Ronde Barber not only played for an incredible 16 seasons with the Buccaneers; he rarely missed a game during that tenure. Barber is the NFL record holder for most consecutive games started by a defensive back, as he started 215 consecutive regular season games (224 total games with playoffs included).

CHAPTER 9:

WHERE'D THEY COME FROM?

QUIZ TIME!

1. Where was legendary Buccaneers cornerback Ronde Barber born?

    a. Liberty City, Florida

    b. Roanoke, Virginia

    c. Niagara Falls, New York

    d. Portland, Oregon

2. Buccaneers linebacker Derrick Brooks, who played 14 years with the team, was born and raised in Pensacola, Florida.

    a. True

    b. False

3. In their first-ever NFL Draft, the Buccaneers selected 20 players. Colleges from which state provided most of their inaugural draft class?

    a. Texas

    b. Florida

c. Utah

d. Georgia

4. Which of the following players has NOT been involved in a trade between the Buccaneers and the New England Patriots?

   a. Tight end Rob Gronkowski

   b. Running back LeGarrette Blount

   c. Quarterback Tom Brady

   d. Tight end Tim Wright

5. From which team did the Buccaneers acquire useful defensive end Jason Pierre-Paul in a 2018 swap?

   a. Jacksonville Jaguars

   b. Seattle Seahawks

   c. Arizona Cardinals

   d. New York Giants

6. Which star Buccaneers defensive lineman was inked as a free agent by the team after leaving the Arizona Cardinals?

   a. End Lee Roy Selmon

   b. Tackle Ndamukong Suh

   c. Tackle Vita Vea

   d. End Simeon Rice

7. The Buccaneers have drafted more players from the Michigan State Spartans than from the Michigan Wolverines over the course of their history.

   a. True

   b. False

8. Which high-profile player dealt in a trade from the Buccaneers to the San Francisco 49ers franchise went on to be elected to the Hall of Fame?

   a. Safety Ronnie Lott
   b. Quarterback Steve Young
   c. Defensive end Richard Dent
   d. Fullback John Henry Johnson

9. One of the Buccaneers' best trades saw them acquire guard Logan Mankins, in exchange for a tight end and a 4th round pick. Which team regretted making that deal with Tampa Bay?

   a. Green Bay Packers
   b. Cleveland Browns
   c. New England Patriots
   d. San Diego Chargers

10. In which city was Bucs franchise quarterback Jameis Winston born in 1994?

    a. Truth or Consequences, New Mexico
    b. Providence, Rhode Island
    c. San Luis Obispo, California
    d. Bessemer, Alabama

11. Two players were teammates in college with the Minnesota Golden Gophers before taking the field together in Tampa Bay as well. Which two players were they?

a. Safety Antonine Winfield Jr. and wide receiver Tyler Johnson

b. Quarterback Josh Freeman and defensive back E.J. Biggers

c. Running back Jeremy McNichols and wide receiver Chris Godwin

d. Linebacker Najee Goode and defensive back Keith Tandy

12. Tampa Bay has never in its history completed a trade with the Kansas City Chiefs.

a. True

b. False

13. In 2004, the Buccaneers traded star wide receiver Keyshawn Johnson to the Dallas Cowboys. Which Cowboy did they receive in return?

a. Wide receiver Michael Clayton

b. Offensive guard Sean Mahan

c. Wide receiver Joey Galloway

d. Free safety Dexter Jackson

14. In 1987, the Buccaneers drafted wide receiver Bruce Hill, who played for Arizona State University, in the 4th round. What was his college team's nickname?

a. Aztecs

b. Fightin' Cacti

c. Sun Devils

d. Coyotes

15. Gerald McCoy, the 3rd overall pick in 2010, played college football as the defensive tackle for which program before coming to the Buccaneers?

    a. Oklahoma Sooners
    b. Nebraska Cornhuskers
    c. Iowa Hawkeyes
    d. Tennessee Volunteers

16. In their entire history, the Buccaneers have never fielded a player who was born in the state of Alaska.

    a. True
    b. False

17. Which prestigious Ivy League college program have the Buccaneers dipped into during the NFL Draft more often than any other?

    a. Harvard University
    b. Dartmouth University
    c. University of Pennsylvania
    d. Yale University

18. From which rival team did the Bucs poach star wide receiver Vincent Jackson as a free agent in 2012?

    a. Tennessee Titans
    b. San Diego Chargers
    c. Minnesota Vikings
    d. Miami Dolphins

19. The talented and flamboyant Keyshawn Johnson was a member of which college squad before his time on the field with the Buccaneers?

a. Notre Dame Fighting Irish

b. Alabama Crimson Tide

c. University of Southern California Trojans

d. Louisiana State Tigers

20. Tampa Bay has completed more trades with the Cincinnati Bengals than with any other NFL franchise.

a. True

b. False

QUIZ ANSWERS

1. B – Roanoke, Virginia

2. A – True

3. A – Texas

4. C – Quarterback Tom Brady

5. D – New York Giants

6. D – End Simeon Rice

7. A – True

8. B – Quarterback Steve Young

9. C – New England Patriots

10. D – Bessemer, Alabama

11. A – Safety Antonine Winfield Jr. and wide receiver Tyler Johnson

12. B – False

13. C – Wide receiver Joey Galloway

14. C – Sun Devils

15. A – Oklahoma Sooners

16. A – True

17. D – Yale University

18. B – San Diego Chargers

19. C – University of Southern California Trojans

20. B – False

DID YOU KNOW?

1. In a very unusual trade in 2002, the Buccaneers sent two 1st round draft picks, two 2nd round draft picks, and $8 million to the Oakland Raiders—for a coach. The hotly debated move paid off though, as new bench boss Jon Gruden immediately led the team to its first-ever Super Bowl victory in his first season on the sidelines.

2. Longtime Bucs safety Donnie Abraham was lucky to be noticed by NFL scouts. Abraham played at East Tennessee State University, a school that does not traditionally receive much attention from NFL teams.

3. The Buccaneers once traded away the 1st overall pick in the NFL Draft. In 1978, they sent this pick to the Houston Oilers, getting great value back by receiving 1st, 2nd, 3rd, and 5th round draft picks along with franchise tight end Jimmie Giles, though the Oilers did get a Hall-of-Famer in running back Earl Campbell with that selection.

4. Tampa Bay and the New York Jets have a rich history of trades throughout the years. Significant names moved between the two teams include wide receiver Keyshawn Johnson, cornerback Darrelle Revis, and defensive tackle Steve McLendon.

5. One of the best free agent signings made by the Buccaneers occurred in 2007 when they wisely inked

undrafted free agent Donald Penn to a deal. Penn took over as the team's starting left tackle and solidified the offensive line for several seasons.

6. In a decision that was very unpopular at the time, Tampa Bay signed free agent wide receiver Alvin Harper to a four-year, $10.6 million dollar deal (which was massive in 1995). Harper played just 25 games for the Bucs, catching only three touchdown passes and failing to justify the big expense.

7. One of the larger and more impactful set of trades ever made by the Buccaneers was completed on draft day in 1995 when the Buccaneers put on a master class. Tampa Bay moved down in the 1st round in a trade with the Philadelphia Eagles and selected defensive tackle Warren Sapp, then moved up into the end of the 1st round again in a deal with the Dallas Cowboys to select linebacker Derrick Brooks. Both players would go on to make the Hall of Fame.

8. Fan-favorite quarterback Doug Williams is the only player the Buccaneers have ever selected who played in college for the Grambling State Tigers.

9. Bucs defensive end Brad Culpepper had very strong ties to the University of Florida, where he has been elected to the Gators Athletic Hall of Fame. His father, grandfather, and uncle all graduated from the school, as did his wife Monica, who was elected the school's homecoming queen in 1991; the same year Culpepper made All-American.

10. Tampa Bay hit the jackpot when they selected linebacker Kwon Alexander 124th overall in 2015. Despite the low draft position, Alexander would be among the Bucs' leading tacklers in each of his first few seasons with the club.

CHAPTER 10:

IN THE DRAFT ROOM

QUIZ TIME!

1. First-ever Buccaneers draft choice Lee Roy Selmon attended the University of Oklahoma, where he played on the Sooners' defensive line along with how many of his brothers?

   a. 0

   b. 1

   c. 2

   d. 3

2. For four consecutive years in the 2000s, the Buccaneers traded out of the 1st round of the NFL Draft, acquiring more proven talent in an effort to compete with the New Orleans Saints.

   a. True

   b. False

3. Of these four Texas programs, from which have the Bucs drafted the most players?

a. Texas Longhorns
b. Texas Tech Red Riders
c. Texas A&M Aggies
d. Texas El Paso Miners

4. During the 1st round of the 2020 NFL Draft, Tampa Bay congratulated which of the following players on becoming a Buccaneer remotely, via webcam, because of the COVID-19 pandemic that prevented the usual handshakes on stage?

   a. Running back Ke'Shawn Vaughn of the Illinois Fighting Illini
   b. Linebacker Joe Tryon of the Washington Huskies
   c. Linebacker Devin White of the LSU Tigers
   d. Offensive tackle Tristan Wirfs of the Iowa Hawkeyes

5. The Buccaneers selected two teammates from the Miami Hurricanes in the 1993 NFL Draft. Which teammates did they choose with the 60th and 104th overall picks?

   a. Defensive end Eric Curry and running back Rudy Harris
   b. Wide receivers Lamar Thomas and Horace Copeland
   c. Quarterback Vinny Testaverde and linebacker Winston Moss
   d. Quarterback Craig Erickson and defensive tackle Warren Sapp

6. How many times in history has Tampa Bay used a top-10 overall draft pick?

a. 13

b. 19

c. 25

d. 30

7. The Bucs have never held the 1st overall pick in the NFL Draft in the entire history of the franchise.

    a. True

    b. False

8. Cornerback Aqib Talib was drafted by the Buccaneers out of which school that is better known as a basketball powerhouse than a football school?

    a. Duke University

    b. University of North Carolina

    c. Gonzaga University

    d. University of Kansas

9. Talented running back Ricky Bell was drafted by Tampa Bay 1st overall in the 1977 NFL Draft. Which Hall of Fame player was selected 2nd overall after the Bucs passed on him for Bell?

    a. Running back Tony Dorsett of the Dallas Cowboys

    b. Defensive back Mike Haynes of the New England Patriots

    c. Wide receiver James Lofton of the Green Bay Packers

    d. Tight end Ozzie Newsome of the Cleveland Browns

10. Only two Ivy League players have played for the Buccaneers after being drafted by them. Which intelligent players made it with Tampa Bay?

a. Offensive tackle JC Tretter of Cornell University and running back Keith Elias of Princeton University

b. Long snapper Zak DeOssie of Brown University and defensive end Marcellus Wiley of Columbia University

c. Wide receiver Justin Watson of the University of Pennsylvania and tight end Nate Lawrie of Yale University

d. Tight end Cameron Brate and quarterback Ryan Fitzpatrick of Harvard University

11. How high did Tampa Bay select Hall of Fame safety John Lynch in the 1993 NFL Draft?

a. 1st round, 6th overall

b. 2nd round, 39th overall

c. 3rd round, 82nd overall

d. 7th round, 224th overall

12. Buccaneers mainstay cornerback Ronde Barber was selected one round after his twin brother, running back Tiki Barber, in the 1997 NFL Draft.

a. True

b. False

13. Which draft choices did the Bucs give up in order to move up and select linebacker Derrick Brooks 28th overall in the 1995 NFL Draft?

a. 32nd and 190th overall

b. 71st, 84th, and 102nd overall

c. 41st and 63rd overall

d. 51st, 83rd, and 177th overall

14. Which of the following is NOT a real school from which Tampa Bay drafted a player during their first two seasons in the NFL?

    a. Minot State University

    b. Washington & Lee University

    c. Southwest Hawaii State University

    d. Lenoir-Rhyne University

15. The Buccaneers drafted two players from the Florida State Seminoles who would go on to play more than 180 NFL games each. Who were these players?

    a. Linebacker Derrick Brooks and running back Warrick Dunn

    b. Defensive back Al Harris and punter Chris Mohr

    c. Wide receiver Mark Carrier and punter Tommy Barnhardt

    d. Defensive back Dexter Jackson and quarterback Jameis Winston

16. Buccaneers linebacker Lavonte David was such a talented athlete coming out of college that he was drafted in not one but three sports (basketball, baseball, and football).

    a. True

    b. False

17. Which team did the Buccaneers trade up with so they could select star linebacker Lavonte David at the NFL Draft in 2012?

a. Jacksonville Jaguars

b. Miami Dolphins

c. Dallas Cowboys

d. Houston Texans

18. In the 1992 NFL Draft, Tampa Bay selected not one but two quarterbacks. Who did they take to attempt to lock down the position?

a. Pat O'Hara of USC and Todd Hammel of Stephen F. Austin

b. Craig Erickson of Miami and Mike Pawlawski of California

c. Trent Dilfer of Fresno State and Shaun King of Tulane

d. Chris Chandler of Washington and Jeff Carlson of Weber State

19. Who did the Tampa Bay Buccaneers select with their two 1st round draft picks in 2012?

a. Linebacker Lavonte David of Nebraska and defensive end Adrian Clayborne of Iowa

b. Defensive tackle Gerald McCoy of Oklahoma and defensive end Da'Quan Bowers of Clemson

c. Wide receiver Mike Evans of Texas A&M and quarterback Mike Glennon of North Carolina State

d. Defensive back Mark Barron of Alabama and running back Doug Martin of Boise State

20. Between 2004 and 2014, Tampa Bay enjoyed a stretch in which they selected at least one player per year who lasted 100 games in the NFL.

a. True
b. False

QUIZ ANSWERS

1. C – 2

2. B – False

3. C – Texas A&M Aggies

4. D – Offensive tackle Tristan Wirfs of the Iowa Hawkeyes

5. B – Wide receivers Lamar Thomas and Horace Copeland

6. B – 19

7. B – False

8. D – University of Kansas

9. A – Running back Tony Dorsett of the Dallas Cowboys

10. C – Wide receiver Justin Watson of the University of Pennsylvania and tight end Nate Lawrie of Yale University

11. C – 3rd round, 82nd overall

12. A – True

13. C – 41st and 63rd overall

14. C – Southwest Hawaii State University

15. A – Linebacker Derrick Brooks and running back Warrick Dunn

16. B – False

17. D – Houston Texans

18. B – Craig Erickson of Miami and Mike Pawlawski of California

19. D – Defensive back Mark Barron of Alabama and running back Doug Martin of Boise State

20. A – True

DID YOU KNOW?

1. In the Buccaneers' first-ever draft, in 1976, the team took two brothers in the 1st and 2nd rounds. Defensive end Lee Roy Selmon was selected 1st overall, and his older brother, linebacker Dewey Selmon, was chosen 60th overall.

2. The most players Tampa Bay has drafted from any school is 14. This mark is held by the University of Alabama Crimson Tide, who have most recently sent solid defensive back Mark Barron and tight end O.J. Howard to the Buccaneers.

3. Tampa Bay has held the 34th overall pick six times; more than any other spot in the draft. Five times they have chosen a player on the offensive side of the ball with that selection, while in 1993, they took linebacker Demetrious DuBose from the University of Notre Dame.

4. Tampa Bay has made two Oklahoma Sooners players top-three picks in the NFL Draft. Both came from the same position group as well, though they were decades apart. The team selected Hall of Fame defensive end Lee Roy Selmon 1st overall in 1976 and defensive tackle Gerald McCoy 3rd overall in 2010.

5. Despite sharing Raymond James Stadium with the team, which makes for the simplest scouting imaginable, the Bucs have never drafted a player from the University of South Florida Bulls.

6. Tampa Bay has drafted precisely seven players who have played a single game in the NFL, including quarterback Joe Hamilton in 2000, who played just four downs in his appearance and finished his career with -2 yards rushing.

7. Of the draft spots in the top 10, Tampa Bay has selected at the 1st overall spot five times; more than any other draft position. Curiously, the Bucs have never picked 2nd overall in their history.

8. The smallest-ever draft class selected by the Buccaneers in the NFL Entry Draft came in 2000 when they took just five players.

9. Twice in franchise history, Tampa Bay has selected 20 players, marking the largest Buccaneers draft classes ever. These were selected in 1976 and 1987, when the team drafted almost enough players over the course of each draft to fill a new starting lineup.

10. The latest pick the Bucs have made in the NFL Draft was quarterback Jack Berry from Washington & Lee University, whom the team chose 460th overall in its first year, 1976. Berry never made it to the NFL. Running back Michael Morton, the team's 325th overall pick from UNLV in 1982, was the latest pick they've made who actually played for the team.

CHAPTER 11:

COACHES, GMS, & OWNERS

QUIZ TIME!

1. Who served as the Buccaneers' first general manager?

    a. Phil Krueger

    b. Leeman Bennett

    c. Hugh Culverhouse

    d. John McKay

2. Tampa Bay general manager Rich McKay once proposed a deal to the New England Patriots that would have sent Buccaneers icon Vinny Testaverde to Massachusetts in exchange for a young and then little-known Tom Brady.

    a. True

    b. False

3. The Bucs' first head coach, John McKay, lasted for how long in that position with the franchise?

    a. 8 games

    b. 2 seasons

    c. 9 seasons

    d. 12 seasons

4. The Buccaneers' most recent coach, Bruce Arians, rose through the coaching ranks at all of the following NCAA programs except for which one?

   a. Florida State Seminoles
   b. Virginia Tech Hokies
   c. Alabama Crimson Tide
   d. Mississippi State Bulldogs

5. Who has owned the Tampa Bay Buccaneers for the longest amount of time?

   a. Malcolm Glazer
   b. Donald Trump
   c. Hugh Culverhouse
   d. Bryan Glazer

6. Of all the Tampa Bay bench bosses who have coached at least two seasons with the team, which one had the lowest winning percentage at only .125?

   a. Lovie Smith
   b. John McKay
   c. Ray Perkins
   d. Leeman Bennett

7. Tampa Bay is the only NFL franchise to have a player rise from competing on the field for the team to ownership of the team.

   a. True
   b. False

8. Which coach led the Buccaneers to their first Super Bowl championship?

a. Bruce Arians

b. Tony Dungy

c. Jon Gruden

d. Sam Wyche

9. Which Tampa Bay general manager once took the field as a player on the team before getting the chance to guide it from the front office?

a. Safety John Lynch

b. Quarterback Trent Dilfer

c. Defensive tackle Warren Sapp

d. No Bucs player has ever been appointed the team's GM.

10. Who is the Tampa Bay leader in all-time coaching wins with the franchise, having recorded 57 regular-season victories?

a. Jon Gruden

b. Tony Dungy

c. John McKay

d. Dirk Koetter

11. For how long did the trio of Fred Cone, Jack Donlan, and Stephen Story act as trustees of Hugh Culverhouse's estate upon Culverhouse's death before finding a permanent new owner for the Buccaneers?

a. 1 year

b. 3 years

c. 6 years

d. 8 years

12. Coach Jon Gruden's 2002 season is the benchmark in terms of winning percentage, as he led the team to a .750 winning percentage in the regular season.

    a. True
    b. False

13. How many of the Buccaneers' head coaches have spent their entire NFL coaching career (interim or permanent) with Tampa Bay?

    a. 0
    b. 2
    c. 5
    d. 10

14. Which Bucs general manager has led the franchise to the most playoff appearances?

    a. Phil Krueger
    b. Rich McKay
    c. Jason Licht
    d. Mark Dominik

15. Out of six seasons coaching the Buccaneers, how many times did coach Tony Dungy finish above .500?

    a. 1
    b. 3
    c. 4
    d. 6

16. At one point in their history, the Buccaneers employed four coaches over a decade who had all started for Tampa Bay at some point during their playing careers.

a. True

b. False

17. How did current team owner Bryan Glazer become the majority owner of the Buccaneers in 2014?

    a. He purchased the team when the previous owners wished to sell.

    b. He inherited the team from his father.

    c. He forced a takeover of the corporation that had previously owned the team.

    d. He was hired as CEO of the company that owned the team.

18. How many head coaches have roamed the sidelines for the Buccaneers in their history?

    a. 6

    b. 9

    c. 12

    d. 21

19. How many Bucs coaches have won an award as the league's top coach, while on the sidelines for Tampa Bay?

    a. 1: Jon Gruden

    b. 2: Jon Gruden and Bruce Arians

    c. 3: Jon Gruden, Bruce Arians, and Tony Dungy

    d. No Tampa Bay coach has ever won this award.

20. Buccaneers owner Malcolm Glazer once proposed trading franchises with New York Yankees owner George Steinbrenner, as part of a business deal.

a. True

b. False

QUIZ ANSWERS

1. D – John McKay

2. B – False

3. C – 9 seasons

4. A – Florida State Seminoles

5. C – Hugh Culverhouse

6. D – Leeman Bennett

7. B – False

8. C – Jon Gruden

9. D – No Bucs player has ever been appointed the team's GM.

10. A – Jon Gruden

11. A – 1 year

12. A – True

13. C – 5

14. B – Rich McKay

15. C – 4

16. B – False

17. B – He inherited the team from his father.

18. C – 12

19. D – No Tampa Bay coach has ever won this award.

20. B – False

DID YOU KNOW?

1. Only once in team history have the Buccaneers fired a coach midway through a season. In 1990, when Tampa Bay was 5-8, the team released coach Ray Perkins, and Richard Williamson, who had been their offensive coordinator, took over. Williamson finished 1-2 but was fired the following season after just a 3-13 record in 1991.

2. Two men have served as both coach and general manager of the Buccaneers. John McKay coached the team for eight years and handled the personnel duties for the first two years of the team's existence before focusing on his sideline duties. Ray Perkins pulled double duty from 1987 to 1990, but the team went 19-41 during his tenure, and he was relieved of both jobs.

3. Tampa Bay Buccaneers owner Malcolm Glazer purchased the team in 1995 for a then-record $192 million. This was not the only sports team Glazer owned, as he also bought the world-famous Manchester United soccer club. While conversion rates fluctuated during his gradual purchase, Manchester United likely cost Glazer slightly more than $1 billion.

4. The Bucs' original general manager, John McKay, left the USC Trojans to build Tampa Bay's organization from scratch as a new NFL franchise. He felt that "within the first week after (I) got to Tampa that (I'd) made a mistake,"

his son noted in a 2007 interview. McKay never found much success with the team but was eventually selected for the Bucs' Ring of Honor, nonetheless.

5. Well-respected head coach Tony Dungy is the only Buccaneers coach to be elected to the Pro Football Hall of Fame. Dungy built the squad that would win Tampa's first Super Bowl the year after he was let go, and later became the first black head coach to claim a Super Bowl victory as the leader of the Indianapolis Colts.

6. Current Bucs head coach Bruce Arians, who has been with the team for just two seasons, has led them to more postseason victories than any other head coach in franchise history.

7. After his time with the Buccaneers, head coach Jon Gruden spent a decade as an analyst on *Monday Night Football*, then signed an unprecedented $100 million, 10-year contract with a no-trade clause to return to coaching with the Oakland Raiders.

8. The Buccaneers have never had a head coach who was born outside the United States. They have also never had a coach who was born in Florida, let alone in Tampa Bay.

9. Tampa Bay head coach Tony Dungy was the first man ever to record a coaching victory against all 32 NFL teams.

10. Never in league history has a Tampa Bay general manager been awarded the Sporting News NFL Executive of the Year Award.

CHAPTER 12:

ODDS & ENDS

QUIZ TIME!

1. Which Buccaneer has won the most league MVP trophies while playing for Tampa Bay?

    a. Linebacker Derrick Brooks

    b. Fullback Mike Alstott

    c. Quarterback Tom Brady

    d. No Tampa Bay player has ever been named the NFL's MVP.

2. The first Buccaneer to win any major award given out by the NFL was franchise defensive tackle Warren Sapp.

    a. True

    b. False

3. During which season did the Buccaneers win their first Vince Lombardi Trophy as Super Bowl champions?

    a. 1979

    b. 1999

    c. 2002

    d. 2020

4. In 2019, the NFL announced its All-Time Team, recognizing the 100 greatest players from the first 100 years of NFL history. How many of these players have suited up for the Bucs?

    a. 3 on offense, 2 on defense, and 0 on special teams
    b. 1 on offense, 4 on defense, and 1 on special teams
    c. 2 on offense, 2 on defense, and 2 on special teams
    d. 4 on offense, 5 on defense, and 0 on special teams

5. What negative event befell cornerback Darrelle Revis before he joined the Buccaneers and won the 2013 Sporting News Comeback Player of the Year Award?

    a. Concussion
    b. Broken femur
    c. Mononucleosis
    d. Torn anterior cruciate ligament

6. What is Emerson Eugene Deckerhoff Jr.'s connection to the Tampa Bay Buccaneers?

    a. An architect who designed and built Raymond James Stadium for the Buccaneers
    b. A beloved groundskeeper who has worked for the Buccaneers since the mid 1980s
    c. A player agent who represented Tom Brady, Rob Gronkowski, and several others
    d. A longtime radio announcer for the Buccaneers on their home station

7. The Tampa Bay Buccaneers have the most wins of any franchise in NFL history.

a. True

b. False

8. Buccaneers quarterbacks Vinny Testaverde and Jameis Winston won the Heisman Trophy while playing at which two rival schools?

   a. University of Alabama and Auburn University
   b. University of Michigan and Ohio State University
   c. University of Miami and Florida State University
   d. University of Washington and Washington State University

9. Only three Buccaneers players have ever won the NFL's Defensive Player of the Year Award while playing with Tampa Bay. Which of the following did NOT take home that trophy?

   a. Cornerback Darrelle Revis
   b. Defensive end Lee Roy Selmon
   c. Linebacker Derrick Brooks
   d. Defensive tackle Warren Sapp

10. Only one player has played an entire career of at least 10 years for the Bucs without ever starting a game for another NFL franchise. Which loyal athlete played only for Tampa Bay?

    a. Defensive tackle Warren Sapp
    b. Defensive end Simeon Rice
    c. Defensive back Ronde Barber
    d. Linebacker Hardy Nickerson

11. Wide receiver Keenan McCardell was a key member of the 2002 championship team in Tampa Bay, but also won an NFL championship while injured with which other franchise?

   a. San Francisco 49ers
   b. Pittsburgh Steelers
   c. Seattle Seahawks
   d. Washington Redskins

12. Tampa Bay is the first NFL team to win the Super Bowl after losing the previous year.

   a. True
   b. False

13. What is the most points the Buccaneers have scored in any Super Bowl?

   a. 24
   b. 31
   c. 48
   d. 53

14. Of the Buccaneers in the Football Hall of Fame, defensive end Lee Roy Selmon is first among them to play with the Bucs. What year did he begin playing with the team?

   a. 1976
   b. 1981
   c. 1986
   d. 1991

15. Kicker Matt Bryant holds the Bucs franchise record for the longest field goal ever made. How long was the record-

setting kick he made to defeat the Philadelphia Eagles as the clock ran out in their 2006 matchup?

a. 55 yards

b. 59 yards

c. 62 yards

d. 66 yards

16. Kicker Martin Gramatica has *missed* more field goals during his Buccaneers career than any other Tampa Bay player has even *attempted*.

a. True

b. False

17. Who was the Bucs' first-ever Super Bowl MVP?

a. Quarterback Tom Brady

b. Quarterback Brad Johnson

c. Defensive tackle Warren Sapp

d. Safety Dexter Jackson

18. Which team has faced off four times against the Buccaneers in the playoffs; more than any other NFL squad?

a. Philadelphia Eagles

b. St. Louis/Los Angeles Rams

c. Dallas Cowboys

d. Washington Football Team

19. Against which opposing team does the Buccaneers franchise have the most all-time victories?

a. New Orleans Saints

b. Minnesota Vikings

c. Detroit Lions

d. Atlanta Falcons

20. The Buccaneers are undefeated in Super Bowl games in which they've partcipated.

a. True

b. False

QUIZ ANSWERS

1. D – No Tampa Bay player has ever been named the NFL's MVP.

2. B – False

3. C – 2002

4. A – 3 on offense, 2 on defense, and 0 on special teams

5. D – Torn anterior cruciate ligament

6. D – A longtime radio announcer for the Buccaneers on their home station

7. B – False

8. C – University of Miami and Florida State University

9. A – Cornerback Darrelle Revis

10. C – Defensive back Ronde Barber

11. D – Washington Redskins

12. B – False

13. C – 48

14. A – 1976

15. C – 62 yards

16. B – False

17. D – Safety Dexter Jackson

18. A – Philadelphia Eagles

19. C – Detroit Lions

20. A – True

DID YOU KNOW?

1. One Buccaneers player has won the NFL's Walter Payton Man of the Year Award. That was linebacker Derrick Brooks, who was honored with the trophy in 2000.

2. In 2021, the Tampa Bay Buccaneers became the first NFL franchise to participate in the Super Bowl while it was being held at their home stadium. Attendance was limited because of the COVID-19 pandemic, but Tampa still used that home field advantage to secure a 31-9 victory over the Kansas City Chiefs.

3. Buccaneers quarterback Tom Brady currently ranks second on the all-time list for most passing yards in the history of the NFL. Brady slots in ahead of his long-time rival Peyton Manning, and just behind former New Orleans Saints quarterback Drew Brees.

4. Although some NFL teams don't use them, Tampa Bay has had a cheerleading squad since its inception in 1976. The Bucs Cheerleaders appear at the team's games and are also active in the community.

5. The Buccaneers' value is estimated at $2.28 billion by *Forbes* magazine, which ranks them as the 29th most valuable NFL team, right between the Tennessee Titans and the Detroit Lions.

6. Buccaneers kicker Connor Barth holds the team's highest field goal percentage (among players with at least 50 kicks attempted), at 83.8% made.

7. Tampa Bay has a winning record against just four other current NFL teams. The Bucs have gotten the better of the Buffalo Bills, Cincinnati Bengals, Miami Dolphins, and Kansas City Chiefs.

8. The Buccaneers have played more regular-season games against the Chicago Bears than any other team in the NFL. The two clubs have faced off 60 times, with Chicago holding a 40-20 record all-time, good for a .667 winning percentage.

9. During the four years between 2013 and 2016, Tampa Bay saw one of its own elected to the Pro Football Hall of Fame every year. Defensive tackle Warren Sapp kicked off the run in 2013, linebacker Derrick Brooks joined him in 2014, 2015 saw both wide receiver Tim Brown and general manager Ron Wolf make the cut, and head coach Tony Dungy capped off the stretch in 2016.

10. Not a single Tampa Bay Buccaneer has ever won the NFL's Offensive Player of the Year Award.

CONCLUSION

There you have it; an amazing collection of Buccaneers trivia, information, and statistics at your fingertips! Regardless of how you fared on the quizzes, we hope that you found this book entertaining, enlightening, and educational.

Ideally, you knew many of these details, but also learned a good deal more about the history of the Tampa Bay Buccaneers, their players, coaches, management, and some of the quirky stories surrounding the team. If you got a little peek into the colorful details that make being a fan so much more enjoyable, then mission accomplished!

The good news is, the trivia doesn't have to stop there! Spread the word. Challenge your fellow Bucs fans to see if they can do any better. Share some of the stories with the next generation to help them become Tampa Bay supporters too.

If you are a big enough Buccaneers fan, consider creating your own quiz with some of the details you know that weren't presented here, and then test your friends to see if they can match your knowledge.

The Tampa Bay Buccaneers are a storied franchise. They have a long history with multiple periods of success, and a few that were less than successful. They've had glorious superstars, iconic moments, hilarious tales. But most of all, they have wonderful, passionate fans. Thank you for being one of them.

Made in the USA
Middletown, DE
13 July 2022

69205392R00076